KATIE MEL[

CALL OFF THE SEARC[

DRAMATICO

in association with

WISE PUBLICATIONS
part of The Music Sales Group

London / New York / Paris / Sydney / Copenhagen / Berlin / Madrid / Tokyo

Published by
Wise Publications
8/9 Frith Street, London W1D 3JB, England.

Exclusive Distributors:
Music Sales Limited
Distribution Centre, Newmarket Road,
Bury St Edmunds, Suffolk IP33 3YB, England.
Music Sales Pty Limited
120 Rothschild Avenue, Rosebery, NSW 2018, Australia.

Order No. AM85390
ISBN 0-7119-2717-0
This book © Copyright 2004 by Wise Publications.

Music arranged by Derek Jones.
Music processed by Paul Ewers Music Design.
Printed in the United Kingdom.

www.musicsales.com

Call Off The Search

Words & Music by Mike Batt

6

world that I see to - day._____ And I've__ got a feel - ing

it won't fade a - way. 3. And I won't

D.S. al Coda

search._____ Now that I've found__ you I'll

Free time

Coda

call off the__ search.

Crawling Up A Hill

Words & Music by John Mayall

Muted Trumpet

1. Ev - 'ry morn - ing 'bout

The Closest Thing To Crazy

Words & Music By Mike Batt

1. How can I think I'm standing strong yet
2. How can you make me fall apart then

feel the air beneath my feet?
break my fall with loving lies?

near - est thing_ to cra - zy I have ev - er known._ I was

nev - er cra - zy on my own___ and

now I know_ that there's a link be - tween_ the two._

Be - ing close_ to cra - zi - ness_ and

My Aphrodisiac Is You

Words & Music by Mike Batt

1. Some peo - ple___ say___ that
2. Don't smoke no___ grass___ or
3. Some peo - ple___ like___ to

oys - ters make you come on___ strong.___ But I don't
o - pi - um from old Hong Kong.___ That hub - ble
read the Kha - ma Su - tra___ first.___ But I don't

buy it, I don't be - lieve my di - et turns___ me___ on.___
bub - ble, just makes me see you dou - ble all___ night long.___
need it, I think if I should read it I'd___ be___ worse.___

21

Al - right,___ I could sniff some pow - dered rhi - no___ horn___ and go to bed in rub - ber gloves._____ But I don't need no___ sti - mu - la - tion, po - tions, balms or___ em - bro - ca - tion. I'm in___ love___ in o - ther words.__

Learnin' The Blues

Words & Music by Dolores Vicki Silvers

Blame It On The Moon

Words & Music by Mike Batt

soon.
-ly.   I was fine,
                                          Guil - ty feel -ings

feel -ing strong,   did -n't want to fall in   love_____
in the night,   as I won -der is it   wrong_____

____ with a -ny -one.
____   to feel so   right?

Now   that it's gone too far to   call for a halt   I'll

So I'll blame it on the moon.

Belfast (Penguins And Cats)

Words & Music by Katie Melua

1. I got a tick - et to the fast ci - ty where the bells don't_ real - ly ring.

(2.) Broad - way go - ing up to Falls where the old man I used to know._

Get - ting

The

Mockingbird Song

Words & Music by Mike Batt
(Based on a traditional lullaby)

(1.) hush now Hon - ey,___ here's the word,___ my Ba - by's gon - na buy me a
2. To this man that___ I have found,___ I'm gon - na sing the
3. When that man and___ I are wed,___ I'm gon - na keep him

mock - ing - bird.___ And if that mock - ing - bird don't_ sing,_
sweet - est_ sound._ And if that sweet - est sound won't_ rock,_
warm in_ bed. And when my man's no long - er_ hot,_

C⁶   F⁶

Ba - by's gon - na buy me a dia - mond_ ring. And_ if_____ that
I'm gon - na buy him a mu - sic_ box. And_ if_____ that
I'm gon - na bring him a vod - ka_ shot. And_ when_____ that

C⁶

dia - mond_ ring_ won't_ shine,_ we'll still have a real good_ time._
mu - sic_ box_ don't_ play,_ he's gon - na stay with me a - ny - way._
spi - rit's_ made_ him strong,_ I'm gon - na stay with him all night_ long.

So I'm sit - ting right   here.
So I'm mak - ing   it   clear.
I'll be hold - ing on   tight - ly.

Woah,_____

oh._____

oh._____

Guitar

D.S. al Coda   Coda

Woah_____

_____ oh._____   Ooh.___

He's gon - na buy____ me a   mock - ing - bird.___

39

I Think It's Going To Rain Today

Words & Music by Randy Newman

think it's go-ing to rain to-day.

Scare-crows dressed_ in the la-test styles_ with fro-zen smiles_ to

chase_ love a-way. Hu-man kind-ness is ov - er flow-ing and I

think it's go-ing to rain to-day. Lone-ly._

41

Tiger In The Night

Words & Music by Mike Batt

Lilac Wine

Words & Music by James Shelton

49

Faraway Voice

Words & Music by Katie Melua

Bringing you the words and the music

All the latest music in print... rock & pop plus jazz, blues, country, classical and the best in West End show scores.

- Books to match your favourite CDs.
- Book-and-CD titles with high quality backing tracks for you to play along to. Now you can play guitar or piano with your favourite artist... or simply sing along!
- Audition songbooks with CD backing tracks for both male and female singers for all those with stars in their eyes.
- Can't read music? No problem, you can still play all the hits with our wide range of chord songbooks.
- Check out our range of instrumental tutorial titles, taking you from novice to expert in no time at all!
- Musical show scores include *The Phantom Of The Opera*, *Les Misérables*, *Mamma Mia* and many more hit productions.
- DVD master classes featuring the techniques of top artists.

Visit your local music shop or, in case of difficulty, contact the Marketing Department, Music Sales Limited, Newmarket Road, Bury St Edmunds, Suffolk, IP33 3YB, UK
marketing@musicsales.co.uk